The Archers

DIARY 2010

F

FRANCES LINCOLN LIMITED
PUBLISHERS

Frances Lincoln Limited
4 Torriano Mews
Torriano Avenue
London NW5 2RZ
www.franceslincoln.com

The Archers Diary 2010

A catalogue record for this book is available from
the British Library

ISBN: 978-07112-3011-8

Printed in China

9 8 7 6 5 4 3 2 1

First Frances Lincoln edition 2009

ACKNOWLEDGMENTS

The Publisher would like to thank Vanessa Whitburn, Editor of
BBC Radio 4's *The Archers*, Producer Kate Oates, Archivist Camilla
Fisher and Hedli Niklaus of Archers Addicts, for their contribution.
Thanks also go to Kathy Brookes of Countryside Art for
permission to use her Ambridge Animals design on the endpapers
and Lesley Saweard for the use of photographs from her private
collection.

ARCHERS ADDICTS

Archers Addicts is the Official Fan Club for BBC Radio 4's *The
Archers*. For further details and a colour brochure, please contact
PO Box 1951, Stratford-upon-Avon, Warwickshire, CV37 1YH
Telephone: 087 087 44400
www.archers-addicts.com

Back cover: SID PERKS (ALAN DEVEREUX) OUTSIDE THE
VILLAGE SHOP

CALENDAR 2010

JANUARY
M	T	W	T	F	S	S
				1	2	3
4	5	6	7	8	9	10
11	12	13	14	15	16	17
18	19	20	21	22	23	24
25	26	27	28	29	30	31

FEBRUARY
M	T	W	T	F	S	S
1	2	3	4	5	6	7
8	9	10	11	12	13	14
15	16	17	18	19	20	21
22	23	24	25	26	27	28

MARCH
M	T	W	T	F	S	S
1	2	3	4	5	6	7
8	9	10	11	12	13	14
15	16	17	18	19	20	21
22	23	24	25	26	27	28
29	30	31				

APRIL
M	T	W	T	F	S	S
			1	2	3	4
5	6	7	8	9	10	11
12	13	14	15	16	17	18
19	20	21	22	23	24	25
26	27	28	29	30		

MAY
M	T	W	T	F	S	S
					1	2
3	4	5	6	7	8	9
10	11	12	13	14	15	16
17	18	19	20	21	22	23
24	25	26	27	28	29	30
31						

JUNE
M	T	W	T	F	S	S
	1	2	3	4	5	6
7	8	9	10	11	12	13
14	15	16	17	18	19	20
21	22	23	24	25	26	27
28	29	30				

JULY
M	T	W	T	F	S	S
			1	2	3	4
5	6	7	8	9	10	11
12	13	14	15	16	17	18
19	20	21	22	23	24	25
26	27	28	29	30	31	

AUGUST
M	T	W	T	F	S	S
						1
2	3	4	5	6	7	8
9	10	11	12	13	14	15
16	17	18	19	20	21	22
23	24	25	26	27	28	29
30	31					

SEPTEMBER
M	T	W	T	F	S	S
		1	2	3	4	5
6	7	8	9	10	11	12
13	14	15	16	17	18	19
20	21	22	23	24	25	26
27	28	29	30			

OCTOBER
M	T	W	T	F	S	S
				1	2	3
4	5	6	7	8	9	10
11	12	13	14	15	16	17
18	19	20	21	22	23	24
25	26	27	28	29	30	31

NOVEMBER
M	T	W	T	F	S	S
1	2	3	4	5	6	7
8	9	10	11	12	13	14
15	16	17	18	19	20	21
22	23	24	25	26	27	28
29	30					

DECEMBER
M	T	W	T	F	S	S
		1	2	3	4	5
6	7	8	9	10	11	12
13	14	15	16	17	18	19
20	21	22	23	24	25	26
27	28	29	30	31		

CALENDAR 2011

JANUARY
M	T	W	T	F	S	S
					1	2
3	4	5	6	7	8	9
10	11	12	13	14	15	16
17	18	19	20	21	22	23
24	25	26	27	28	29	30
31						

FEBRUARY
M	T	W	T	F	S	S
	1	2	3	4	5	6
7	8	9	10	11	12	13
14	15	16	17	18	19	20
21	22	23	24	25	26	27
28						

MARCH
M	T	W	T	F	S	S
	1	2	3	4	5	6
7	8	9	10	11	12	13
14	15	16	17	18	19	20
21	22	23	24	25	26	27
28	29	30	31			

APRIL
M	T	W	T	F	S	S
				1	2	3
4	5	6	7	8	9	10
11	12	13	14	15	16	17
18	19	20	21	22	23	24
25	26	27	28	29	30	

MAY
M	T	W	T	F	S	S
						1
2	3	4	5	6	7	8
9	10	11	12	13	14	15
16	17	18	19	20	21	22
23	24	25	26	27	28	29
30	31					

JUNE
M	T	W	T	F	S	S
		1	2	3	4	5
6	7	8	9	10	11	12
13	14	15	16	17	18	19
20	21	22	23	24	25	26
27	28	29	30			

JULY
M	T	W	T	F	S	S
				1	2	3
4	5	6	7	8	9	10
11	12	13	14	15	16	17
18	19	20	21	22	23	24
25	26	27	28	29	30	31

AUGUST
M	T	W	T	F	S	S
1	2	3	4	5	6	7
8	9	10	11	12	13	14
15	16	17	18	19	20	21
22	23	24	25	26	27	28
29	30	31				

SEPTEMBER
M	T	W	T	F	S	S
			1	2	3	4
5	6	7	8	9	10	11
12	13	14	15	16	17	18
19	20	21	22	23	24	25
26	27	28	29	30		

OCTOBER
M	T	W	T	F	S	S
					1	2
3	4	5	6	7	8	9
10	11	12	13	14	15	16
17	18	19	20	21	22	23
24	25	26	27	28	29	30
31						

NOVEMBER
M	T	W	T	F	S	S
	1	2	3	4	5	6
7	8	9	10	11	12	13
14	15	16	17	18	19	20
21	22	23	24	25	26	27
28	29	30				

DECEMBER
M	T	W	T	F	S	S
			1	2	3	4
5	6	7	8	9	10	11
12	13	14	15	16	17	18
19	20	21	22	23	24	25
26	27	28	29	30	31	

INTRODUCTION

From humble Hollowtree Farm (right) to all the grandeur of Lower Loxley Hall, Ambridge is many things to many people. At its heart for all of us however, lies a rich and diverse farming community, whose activities keep us glued to our radios week after week.

The Archers Diary 2010 highlights some of the people who contribute to the colour and texture of Ambridge's daily life, and describes the places in which they live. The Snells of Ambridge Hall, the Tuckers at Willow Farm, the Carters in Ambridge View and the Lloyds at The Stables; all these people have their counterparts in real life and reflect some of the pleasure and pain of living in a rural village in the 21st century.

The village grapevine works over-time and privacy can be hard to come by. However, Mike and Neil lend each other a helping hand at times of need, a chat with Jill solves all sorts of problems and even Brian Aldridge has been known to put himself out to help Jack and Peggy Woolley. The pleasure for the listener is in escaping daily life and immersing ourselves in somebody else's story – even if it is only for fifteen minutes a day!

The Archers Diary gives you the chance to record your own important dates alongside those of your favourite characters, while enjoying stunning rural images inspired by the series and finding out more about *The Archers.*

Archers Addicts
Official fan club for BBC Radio 4's *The Archers*
www.archers-addicts.com

The

Borchester Echo

SOUVENIR COPY

PRICE 6d.   AND FELPERSHAM GAZETTE   SEPTEMBER, 1958

THE ARCHERS CELEBRATE
2,000 BROADCASTS

Successful BBC Serial

Dan Archer (Harry Oakes) and Doris (Gwen Berryman) pose for a special picture at the gate of Brookfield Farm on the eve of the 2,000th episode of "The Archers" which has been broadcast daily by the BBC since New Year's Day, 1951.

MR. & MRS. DANIEL ARCHER, of Brookfield Farm, Ambridge, whose day-to-day activities are overheard each night by between six and seven million listeners to the Light Programme, will take part in the two thousandth episode of 'The Archers' on Friday evening, September 26th. They will be joined by their son, Mr. Philip Archer, their daughter, Mrs. Christine Johnson, and by such well-known friends and neighbours as Mr. Walter Gabriel and Mr. Tom Forrest.

Friday's 2,000th fifteen-minute broadcast means that the programme has been heard for five days a week in the Light Programme ever since January 1st, 1951.

Two thousand episodes means that the programme's total transmission time amounts to 500 hours or nearly 21 days.

'The Archers' was first thought of in Birmingham. The seed was sown at a meeting held in the Midland capital to consider the future policy for agricultural programmes. A Lincolnshire farmer startled everyone by saying that British agriculture might be best served by a serial programme, "a sort of farming Dick Barton."

He maintained that the farmer's seasonal struggle with weather and the diseases that attack crops and livestock could be made as exciting as any thriller serial.

Making notes

Godfrey Baseley, then agricultural producer for Midland Region, listened intently. Before the meeting was over, he was already jotting down notes on the pad in front of him . . .

In Whit Week, 1950, 'The Archers' was given a trial run—in the morning. There were five episodes—and they were a success. So much so that on the first day of the following year, 'The Archers' was launched in the Light Programme.

A programme, which has in some senses become a part of the national life, is bound to have had a varied and exciting history. The following dates are landmarks in its growth.

January, 1954—Tied with 'Take it from Here' for 'Daily Mail' National Radio Award.

November, 1954—1,000th edition.

January, 1955—Sole winners of 'Daily Mail' National Radio Award.

September, 1955 — Tragic death of Mrs. Grace Archer (which became headline news in Great Britain's national newspapers).

February, 1957—The holding of Tom Forrest on a charge of murder (also a national newspaper story).

Mason and Webb, working on a month-on, month-off basis, have written all the scripts so far. Although they live 200 miles apart, and rarely see each other except at script conferences in Birmingham, they work harmoniously together and without difficulty. Says Ted Mason: "We served a pretty tough apprenticeship together, Dick Barton from 1946 until March, 1951!"

Both Bob and Tom are Coin Collectors!

WHEN Tom Forrest first mentioned in 'The Archers' that he collected Roman coins, one or two kind-hearted listeners sent him a handful of coins which they no longer had any use for. And Bob Arnold, who plays Tom Forrest, was delighted. . .

For Bob Arnold is a collector of Roman coins. In fact, he has the largest private collection of Roman coins in the country.

The authors would be the first to admit that Tom Forrest would never have become a numismatist had not Roman coins been Bob Arnold's hobby.

"Most men have some sort of hobby," author Ted Mason told an 'Echo' reporter, "and we find it saves time and trouble if, when possible, we make the character have the same hobby as the actor who plays him. Then if we want any information about that hobby, all we have to do is ask the actor."

Philip Garston-Jones, who plays the well-loved Mr. Sproggett, is himself a bird watcher. In fact, it was his own interest in ornithology which inspired the introduction of Sproggett into the story.

"I happened to mention to Godfrey Baseley and Ted Mason that it seemed a pity bird-spotting had never been referred to in 'The Archers'", said Philip Garston-Jones, "They were both taken with the idea at once, but I didn't dream that within a few weeks I myself would be playing the bird-spotter and supplying them with information about birds."

Borchester Echo

PROPRIETOR: J WOOLLEY

LOVE TRAGEDY FOR LOCAL PIG FARMER

Hayley Jordan and John Archer

In a further twist to the tragedy of young Ambridge farmer John Archer (22), killed last month in a tractor accident while working on his father's farm, it has now come to light that on the evening before he died, he proposed to his long standing girl friend Hayley Jordan.

The ECHO has learnt that the dead man's parents, Pat and Tony Archer, found a photograph of Hayley and an exquisite sapphire engagement ring in a velvet-lined box, while clearing out their son's personal effects at April Cottage. John and Hayley had lived there together for some time.

BROKEN RELATIONSHIP

The couple had broken up, but in an attempt at reconciliation they met to have dinner together at the Mont Blanc Restaurant near Waterley Cross. It was during the meal that John proposed marriage, but was turned down by Hayley. Last night Hayley was still too devastated to make any comment on whether this might have had any bearing on the accident.

The Inspector of the Health and Safety Executive is still investigating the circumstances of the accident which happened on 25 February at Bridge Farm, Ambridge, when the vintage tractor John Archer was driving, overturned, crushing him beneath it.

It is understood that the Inspector has made a further visit to the site during the past week.

INQUEST TO FOLLOW

The Coroner's Office at Felpersham told the ECHO that they expected the inquest into Mr Archer's death to take place in about five weeks' time.

The Farm Shop at Bridge Farm has taken down its notice announcing its closure due to the bereavement. It now has a sign saying that it will not re-open, and thanking past customers for their support. The shop, run by Mrs Pat Archer, attracted customers from a wide area who came for its organic fruit, vegetables and yoghurt.

PIG VENTURE CONTINUING

Friends and relatives of the late John Archer have banded together to ensure that his several farming projects are kept going. It is hoped that his younger brother Mr Thomas Archer helped by John Archer's former girlfriend, Hayley Jordan, will take over the running of the highly successful organic pig units at Bridge Farm.

COVERDALE CLOBBERS CLIVE

REPORT BY OUR CRIME CORRESPONDENT NATHAN JONES

AMBRIDGE MAN GETS FIVE YEARS.
CO-DEFENDANTS ESCAPE WITH THREE YEARS.

After a long and somewhat acrimonious trial, Clive Horrobin (25) of The Green, Ambridge, was sentenced to five years imprisonment for causing Grievous Bodily Harm to George Barford, gamekeeper at the Grey Gables estate, Ambridge.

DASTARDLY ATTACK
Sentencing him, the Judge Mr Justice Brooke said that Horrobin had been the ringleader in a dastardly and pointless attack by three young men on an elderly man who could have died from the injuries he had received. As it was, there was some doubt as to whether Mr Barford would ever completely recover.
What made matters worse was that Horrobin had gone to considerable

THE VICTIM GEORGE BARFORD

lengths to establish a false alibi so putting an entirely innocent member of the public under suspicion.

LENIENT SENTENCE
The Judge said that he had taken into account that Horrobin had admitted causing grievous bodily harm, but denied "intent to cause serious injury". And considering Horrobin's past record five years could be described as a somewhat lenient sentence. The co-defendants in the case, Terry Fielding (25) a school friend of Horrobin's, and Ramsey Wilson (23), both of Felpersham were each given three years for the lesser offence of assault.

COVERDALE COMMENDED
At the end of the trial the Judge commended Detective Inspector James Coverdale for his painstaking work in bringing the culprits to justice.
DI Coverdale told the ECHO: "I had no doubt in my mind whatsoever at any time that Clive Horrobin was the main offender."

THE SUN HAS GOT HIS HAT ON!

The recent sunny days have been a welcome change in the weather even though we are still in March. The staff of the Promenade restaurant in Borchester were brave enough to bring tables and chairs outside onto the pavement where they were quickly occupied by customers taking morning coffee.

Borchester weatherman Adrian Corby warns us that we've not seen the end of the winter yet and the sharp northerly winds will soon return.

INSPECTOR JAMES COVERDALE

BIRTHDAYS AND ANNIVERSARIES

JANUARY

APRIL

FEBRUARY

MAY

MARCH

JUNE

JULY

OCTOBER

AUGUST

NOVEMBER

SEPTEMBER

DECEMBER

CHRISTMAS

THE ULTIMATE CONTACT SHEET

FAMILY

Name ....   Name ....   Name ....   Name ....

H ....   H ....   H ....   H ....

W ....   W ....   W ....   W ....

M ....   M ....   M ....   M ....

Name ....   Name ....   Name ....   Name ....

H ....   H ....   H ....   H ....

W ....   W ....   W ....   W ....

M ....   M ....   M ....   M ....

WORK CONTACTS

....

....

....

NEIGHBOURS   ## DOCTOR   ## DENTIST

....

....

....

OPTICIAN   ## HOSPITAL   ## POLICE STATION   ## LOCAL COUNCIL

....

....

....

BANKS

....
....
....

BUILDING SOCIETIES

MORTGAGE LENDER/LANDLORD

....
....
....

FAVOURITE RESTAURANTS/TAKEAWAYS

....
....
....

OTHER USEFUL NUMBERS

....
....
....
....
....
....
....
....

USEFUL LINKS

BBC Radio 4 *The Archers* – Official BBC Archers site, includes a listen-again facility and podcast download: www.bbc.co.uk/radio4/archers

Archers Addicts – Official fan club for *The Archers*, featuring the Village Shop, on-line fan club newspaper, competitions, Ambridge gossip and forums: www.archers-addicts.com

ACTORS' SITES

Timothy Bentinck (David Archer) features a personal site crammed with information about all his other interests and work besides *The Archers*: www.bentinck.net

Terry Molloy (Mike Tucker) has a site which combines Ambridge with *Dr Who* (hear Davros!): www.terrymolloy.co.uk

Felicity Jones (Emma Grundy) has a strong following. This site keeps you up to date on all her latest projects: http://myweb.tiscali.co.uk/chevron/felicityjones/index.html

BORSETSHIRE BRAINTEASERS

AMBRIDGE ANIMALS

TRICKY!

Can you tell your Dawkin from your Sussex? Unscramble the words below to reveal some popular cattle and pig breeds and wow the likes of Ed Grundy with your supreme knowledge. Give yourself a point for every right answer (answers on page 128).

CATTLE

ENERGY US
FAINER IS
RE OF HERD

PIGS

BRISK HERE
HI MILD TWEED
CEDE GHOSTLIER POLO RUSTS

YOU'RE AN ANIMAL!

EASY!

Animals need a lot of care and the hard working husbandmen and women of Ambridge have got themselves in a muddle. Can you rearrange the letters below to discover who they are? One point for each correct answer (answers on page 128).

LEG IN
OMT
JE RAZZ

LN DAY
LAY HEY
HURT

CREATURE COMFORTS WORDSEARCH

We can't help but love our pets, and the residents of Ambridge are no exception. Over the years, Ambridge has been home to the customary cats and dogs and some more exotic visitors including snakes and even elephants.

Solve the clues below to reveal the names of twelve beloved Ambridge animals, then find them in the word search opposite. There are a few letters in each clue to get you started. Don't forget to award yourself a point for each correct answer (answers on page 128).

1. Joe has st**artle**d many a passer-**by** with the clatter of his trap pulled by this long serving pony:

   _ _ _ _ _ _ _ _

2. Eddie has an **arch** sense of humour, naming one of his favourite ferrets after this matriarchal Ambridge resident: _ _ _ / _ _ _ _ _ _

3. Remem**ber** when this creature caused a stir as it slithered into Ambridge? Clarrie **tie**d herself in knots when she saw it! _ _ _ _ _ _

4. Few who heard it will forget the dramatic **night** when Grace saved Christine's favourite horse from a terrible fire: _ _ _ _ _ _ _ _

5. It's no **lie** that Lynda was full of joy when Constanza gave birth to this lovely little llama and she **sal**lied forth to tell her friends! _ _ _ _ _ _ _

6. No **les**s than beautiful, this proud bird struts his stuff to an adoring public at The Bull: _ _ _ _ _ _

7. Alistair must have been a bit **har**d up when he gave Daniel this hai**ry** little hamster! _ _ _ _ _

8. Nigel thinks this addition to the Lower Loxley contingent is a real 'gem'. **Crane** your neck to see her; she could probably **ford** the river Am! _ _ _ _ _ _ _ _ / _ _ _ _ _ _ _

9. It was said that, **in a**ll ways, Mrs. Antrobus thought Afghans were **bett**er than people, and she certainly loved this hound: _ _ _ _ _ _ _

10. Alice bent her father's **ear** until he gave her this **sp**ecial show jumper: _ _ _ _ _ _ _ _ _

11. The name of this **emi**nent visitor to Ambridge Hall (aka 'Duckingham Palace') was inspired by a popular Beatrix Potter character: _ _ _ _ _ _

12. Susan and Neil were brought together by this **pink** piggy which Susan won at the village fete: _ _ _ _ _

E	M	F	M	A	M	E	J	B	S	O	H	E	U	C	R	P	S
C	I	S	R	W	I	G	J	R	E	H	C	R	A	S	R	M	A
S	E	V	A	L	N	P	B	S	A	T	N	Y	T	A	F	A	R
P	C	O	S	I	M	I	D	N	I	G	H	T	W	L	O	N	D
L	C	R	E	P	A	S	M	G	I	E	O	P	R	I	Q	B	E
I	L	K	A	E	B	B	I	F	R	G	S	A	C	E	E	Q	D
S	E	L	R	N	M	E	T	Y	J	P	T	K	P	R	I	O	J
N	S	I	J	E	F	C	S	C	E	L	N	H	T	I	F	T	S
B	T	A	T	S	P	O	N	A	M	K	P	I	S	E	H	A	E
P	K	E	L	I	R	S	R	I	A	P	E	Y	O	S	R	C	Y
O	Y	U	B	T	D	M	N	D	E	B	W	L	A	M	T	H	B
R	I	A	E	M	I	S	R	B	C	A	L	R	N	J	L	R	E
T	P	R	T	N	V	H	L	A	L	R	T	Y	I	E	P	O	L
S	H	I	T	E	I	J	M	E	A	L	Y	C	L	M	C	V	T
N	T	G	I	C	C	B	L	H	O	K	J	S	D	I	B	L	R
A	M	C	N	L	R	S	K	Y	N	E	T	N	T	M	P	S	A
Y	R	R	A	H	T	Y	A	I	P	X	N	E	B	A	I	R	B
U	E	W	R	S	R	E	P	R	A	R	S	M	O	Y	L	T	E

HOW DID YOU SCORE? (answers on page 128)

♔♔♔♔ 19–24

Keep on purring because you're the cat that got the cream! Your excellent diet of omega enriched fish has obviously fuelled your brain – well done!

♔♔♔ 12–18

Like Jack's favourite dog, Captain, you are enthusiastic, energetic and give your all. You're not as quick as a cat, but you chew over a problem like a tasty bone and get there in the end – good effort!

♔♔ 6–11

Don't get in a flap! You tried to wing it but I'm afraid your feathers got ruffled. Try again another time and in the meantime give your bird brain a boost!

♔ 0–5

Come out of hibernation, you've missed some episodes! Although they say the tortoise won the race, you have to speed up to keep up!

THE STABLES
The Lloyds

PRESENT DAYS

When she was young, Phil and Jill hoped Shula would train to be a vet but, showing her stubborn streak, she ended up marrying one instead. Mind you, some could argue it was a canny move as she now has a personal consultant on hand to keep the horses in fine fettle.

Like many young girls Shula adored horses and loved to help out at her cousin Lilian's riding stables. She was a keen horsewoman and in 1974, British show jumper Ann Moore declared that Shula had the potential to become a professional rider but noted that she was rather headstrong. However, life took her down a different path and she wound up as an office junior at Rodway & Watsons estate agents. It wasn't until 2001 that she returned to her first love, buying The Stables from her Aunt, Christine Barford. Fortunately, she'd completed a horse management course in her youth, and it didn't take long for her to brush up her skills and start teaching riding lessons.

Alistair and Shula have had some tricky times, not least in dealing with Alistair's gambling addiction. They haven't been helped by Alistair's father, Professor Jim Lloyd, who knows how to torment Shula to a nicety and is a dubious role model for her son Daniel. Daniel was unsettled when Alistair proposed to Shula in 1999, but their relationship improved and Alistair adopted Daniel in 2000. The family has settled down at The Stables which provides a workplace for both Shula and Alistair since he relocated his veterinary practice in the grounds.

Shula and Alistair (Judy Bennett and Michael Lumsden)

PAST TIMES

- The Stables was developed from land once owned by Fred Barratt, a farmer who formed a company with Phil and Dan Archer known as Ambridge Farmers Ltd. Plagued by ill health, Fred took early retirement and sold part of the farm to Laura Archer who allowed Lilian to develop a riding school in the grounds.

- When Laura moved to Ambridge Hall in 1973, Lilian bought both property and land from her Aunt and renamed it The Stables. Having studied at the Felpersham Riding Academy, Lilian was determined to establish a successful school.

- Christine helped Lilian run the riding school until Lilian left Ambridge with Ralph Bellamy two years later. Phil and Dan seized the opportunity to invest on Christine's behalf, giving her some stability while her husband, Paul Johnson, headed for bankruptcy. After Paul's death, Christine went on to marry George Barford and they continued living in The Stables farmhouse.

Above, Christine (Lesley Saweard), Ann Moore, Lilian (Elizabeth Marlowe) and Shula (Judy Bennett)

OFF AIR:

Judy Bennett who plays Shula is married to Charles Collingwood better known as Brian Aldridge… and you thought The Archers family tree was complicated!

One of the sound supervisors told us the most bizarre sound effect they ever had to create was 'rasping a horse's teeth'; in the end they used a large file against a bone inside a box. It did the trick!

The actors tell us that they feel quite foolish perched on a saddle on a stool pretending they're on the back of a horse. Are there no lengths to which they won't go?

DECEMBER | JANUARY

---

28 Monday

Holiday, UK
GODFREY BASELEY PRESENTED 'INTRODUCING *THE ARCHERS*' 1950

---

29 Tuesday

---

30 Wednesday

---

31 Thursday

Full Moon
New Year's Eve
JOHN ARCHER BORN 1975

---

1 Friday

New Year's Day
Holiday, UK, Republic of Ireland, Canada, USA,
Australia and New Zealand
JACK AND PEGGY WOOLLEY MARRIED 1991
THE ARCHERS FIRST BROADCAST NATIONWIDE 1951

---

2 Saturday

---

3 Sunday

4 Monday

Holiday, Scotland (subject to confirmation)
Holiday, New Zealand

5 Tuesday

6 Wednesday

Epiphany

7 Thursday

Last Quarter
JENNIFER ALDRIDGE BORN 1945

8 Friday

9 Saturday

10 Sunday

PAT ARCHER BORN 1952

JANUARY

11 Monday

12 Tuesday

13 Wednesday

14 Thursday

15 Friday   *New Moon*

16 Saturday

17 Sunday   GEORGE BARFORD DIED 2005

18 Monday   Holiday, USA (Martin Luther King's Birthday)

19 Tuesday   NOLUTHANDO MADIKANE BORN 2001

20 Wednesday

21 Thursday   BRENDA TUCKER BORN 1981

22 Friday

23 Saturday   *First Quarter*

24 Sunday

JOLENE AND SID PERKS (BUFFY DAVIS AND ALAN DEVEREUX)

25 Monday

---

26 Tuesday

Holiday, Australia (Australia Day)

---

27 Wednesday

---

28 Thursday

---

29 Friday

---

30 Saturday

Full Moon
KATHY PERKS BORN 1953

---

31 Sunday

STABLE FARE
SHULA HEBDEN LLOYD

"This Steak and Onion Casserole is one of Mum's brilliant recipes and it's been well and truly tried and tested. It's simple to prepare and leaves me free to get on with lessons while it slowly tenderises in the oven. It really warms you up if you've been outside in the cold all day."

Serves 2–4

INGREDIENTS

1lb braising steak cut into 4 pieces (from Brookfield of course)
150g (6oz) bacon, cubed
1 tbsp oil
2 onions
3 medium sized carrots, sliced
3 cloves of garlic, crushed
125g (5fl oz) stout
½ tsp Worcestershire sauce
Seasoned flour
Salt & freshly milled black pepper

METHOD

- Preheat oven to 140°C (Gas mark 1)
- Coat meat on both sides with seasoned flour. Heat oil in casserole dish until sizzling hot. Brown beef on both sides then set aside.
- Fry bacon and onions until brown. Add carrots and garlic, then arrange the meat on top. Add any meat juices and season with salt and pepper.
- Add the stout and put the lid on the casserole. Place in the oven to cook for approx 2½ hours until the meat is tender.

☆ SHULA'S TOP TIP ☆

Try stirring in a tablespoon of cider vinegar before serving for some extra zing!

FEBRUARY

WEEK 6
2010

1 Monday

2 Tuesday

ROY TUCKER BORN 1978

3 Wednesday

4 Thursday

5 Friday

Last Quarter

6 Saturday

Accession of Queen Elizabeth II
Holiday, New Zealand (Waitangi Day)

7 Sunday

FEBRUARY

WEEK 7
2010

8 Monday

9 Tuesday

WILLIAM GRUNDY BORN 1983

10 Wednesday

11 Thursday

12 Friday

13 Saturday

14 Sunday

New Moon
St. Valentine's Day
Chinese New Year

15 Monday

Holiday, USA (Washington's Birthday)

16 Tuesday

Shrove Tuesday
TONY ARCHER BORN 1951

17 Wednesday

Ash Wednesday
PIP ARCHER BORN 1993
MARK HEBDEN DIED 1994

18 Thursday

19 Friday

20 Saturday

MARK HEBDEN BORN 1955

21 Sunday

FEBRUARY

22 Monday   *First Quarter*

23 Tuesday

24 Wednesday

25 Thursday   TOM ARCHER BORN 1981
NEIL AND SUSAN CARTER MARRIED 1984
JOHN ARCHER DIED 1998

26 Friday

27 Saturday

28 Sunday   *Full Moon*

LYNDA SNELL (CAROLE BOYD)

MARCH

1 Monday

St. David's Day
CHRISTINE AND GEORGE BARFORD MARRIED 1979

2 Tuesday

3 Wednesday

4 Thursday

5 Friday

6 Saturday

7 Sunday

Last Quarter
ABIGAIL TUCKER BORN 2008

8 Monday

9 Tuesday

10 Wednesday

11 Thursday

12 Friday

13 Saturday

14 Sunday

Mothering Sunday, UK

DEBBIE AND BRIAN ALDRIDGE (TAMSIN GREIG AND CHARLES COLLINGWOOD) IN STUDIO

15 Monday

New Moon
EDDIE GRUNDY BORN 1951
BENJAMIN ARCHER BORN 2002

16 Tuesday

17 Wednesday

St. Patrick's Day
Holiday, Northern Ireland and Republic of Ireland

18 Thursday

NEWS OF NELSON GABRIEL'S DEATH 2001

19 Friday

20 Saturday

Vernal Equinox (Spring begins)

21 Sunday

MARCH

22 Monday

---

23 Tuesday   *First Quarter*

---

24 Wednesday

---

25 Thursday

---

26 Friday

---

27 Saturday

---

28 Sunday   British Summer Time begins
                                                                      Palm Sunday

AMBRIDGE HALL
The Snells

PRESENT DAYS

Having fallen in love with its Victorian charm, the Snells snapped up Ambridge Hall in 1986 for a mere £160,000. It's no surprise that on Lynda's first day in Ambridge, she managed to ruffle the feathers of both Eddie Grundy and Brian Aldridge; little did they know then that this was just a taste of things to come! Robert's gentle nature however, caused much less of a stir. Seeing him frequently submit to the powerful will of his wife, some wondered whether Lynda would make him sleep in the old servants' quarters at the Hall, but Robert's clearly more assertive than he seems.

Lynda is a professional campaigner, annoying most of the villagers, most of the time. Fortunately Ambridge Hall takes up her energies too and reflects her many other interests. She's renovated the Hall according to the guiding principles of feng shui – who can forget Robert trying to find his bed? She's incorporated a dramatic water feature into her garden, and created a low allergen area for her fellow hay fever sufferers; she really thinks of everything.

When Robert was made redundant in 2006, the Snells had to re-think their lifestyle. With six bedrooms Ambridge Hall is a large property for two, so they decided to run it as a Bed and Breakfast. Of course Lynda strives to maintain the very highest standards and her guests receive far more than a simple breakfast. Advice and suggestions for how to spend their time in Ambridge is thrown in for free. And guests are in for a surprise when they wander round the paddock. Adding her own unique twist to the Ambridge countryside, Lynda eschewed the common sheep, choosing instead to tend Anglo-Nubian goats Persephone and Demeter, and more recently, lovely llamas Wolfgang, Constanza and Salieri.

Lynda (Carole Boyd) campaigns with *Restoration*'s Griff Rhys Jones

Laura Archer (Betty McDowall)

Colonel Frederick Danby (Ballard Berkeley)

PAST TIMES

- Although it's hard to imagine, there was once a time, a peaceful time, before the haughty sniffs and proud opinions of Lynda Snell reverberated through Ambridge. Built in 1860 by the Lawson-Hopes, the Hall was initially home to the local doctor.

- Carol Grenville inherited the house when husband, Charles, died in 1965. She sold it to Jack Woolley when she married John Tregorran two years later. One of Ambridge's most popular couples, the production team are still asked for the whereabouts of the Tregorrans (they moved to Bristol in 1990).

- Some years later the Hall provided shelter for Ambridge's 'odd couple', Laura Archer and Colonel Frederick Danby (Ballard Berkeley). Laura wanted to leave the Hall to Danby but, due to complications with her will, the property went to Laura's great-niece who promptly put it on the market. Just think, if Laura had signed the will, the Snells may never have moved to Ambridge . . .

OFF AIR:

Refined bachelor, Colonel Danby, was much loved by many listeners, as well as many single women in Ambridge. Not many people know that Norman Shelley, the first actor to play Danby, was also the voice of Winnie the Pooh for The Children's Hour *adaptation of A.A. Milne's classic.*

The role of Danby clearly attracted charismatic actors as it was later taken up by the wonderful Ballard Berkeley. Ballard was best known for his portrayal of another retired military man; he played Major Gowen in the definitive British comedy, Fawlty Towers.

Another versatile Archers actor is Graham Blockey who not only plays Robert Snell, but in real life is a fully fledged GP.

29 Monday

---

30 Tuesday

Full Moon
First Day of Passover (Pesach)
JAMES BELLAMY BORN 1973

---

31 Wednesday

---

1 Thursday

Maundy Thursday

---

2 Friday

Good Friday
Holiday, UK, Canada, Australia and New Zealand
GRACE ARCHER BORN 1929

---

3 Saturday

Holiday, Australia
CAROLINE STERLING BORN 1955

---

4 Sunday

Easter Sunday

5 Monday

Easter Monday Holiday, UK (exc. Scotland), Republic of Ireland,
Canada, Australia and New Zealand
Seventh Day of Passover (Pesach)
ROBERT SNELL BORN 1943

6 Tuesday

Last Quarter
Eighth Day of Passover (Pesach)

7 Wednesday

GEORGE GRUNDY BORN 2005

8 Thursday

9 Friday

10 Saturday

11 Sunday

PHIL AND GRACE ARCHER MARRIED 1955

APRIL

12 Monday

KATE AND LUCAS MADIKANE MARRIED 2001
FIRST SUNDAY EPISODE 1998

13 Tuesday

14 Wednesday

New Moon

15 Thursday

16 Friday

HELEN ARCHER BORN 1979

17 Saturday

18 Sunday

19 Monday

OMNIBUS LENGTHENED TO 1HR 15 MINS 1998

20 Tuesday

21 Wednesday

First Quarter
Birthday of Queen Elizabeth II
ELIZABETH PARGETTER BORN 1967

22 Thursday

23 Friday

St. George's Day
PHIL ARCHER BORN 1928
DAN ARCHER DIED 1986

24 Saturday

KATHY AND SID PERKS MARRIED 1987

25 Sunday

Anzac Day, Australia and New Zealand

LYNDA'S CHEZ D'OEUFS
LYNDA SNELL

"The greasy fry up fails to meet the needs of a distinguished visitor, so spread some class with this peerless recipe. Your guests, like mine, will find waking up to these wonderful Benedictine *Oeufs* a truly unforgettable experience. As any *cordon bleu* chef will tell you, eggs must be fresh and free range, and do try to use organic ingredients wherever possible."

Serves 2

INGREDIENTS

4 large free range eggs
2 toasting muffins
3 tbsp white wine vinegar
1 batch hot hollandaise sauce
4 slices Parma ham
Fresh chives

METHOD

- Bring a deep saucepan of water to boil, add vinegar. Break each egg into a ramekin. Split muffins, toast them and warm plates.
- Swirl saucepan to create a vortex of water and slide in first egg; it should curl into a ball. Cook for 2–3 minutes then carefully remove with a slotted spoon. Repeat with remaining eggs.
- Spread muffins with hollandaise sauce, delicately drape ribbon of ham on top, then finish with egg. Spoon over remaining hollandaise and garnish with snipped chives, fresh from the garden.

☆ LYNDA'S TOP TIP ☆

I know bought hollandaise is easier, but there is no substitute for the real thing and you can find a recipe in most good cook books. I always say that with a little patience and care, your guests will always come back for more.

26 Monday

Holiday, Australia (Anzac Day)

27 Tuesday

28 Wednesday

Full Moon

29 Thursday

30 Friday

1 Saturday

HAYLEY TUCKER BORN 1977

2 Sunday

MAY

3 Monday   Early Spring Bank Holiday, UK and Republic of Ireland

4 Tuesday

5 Wednesday

6 Thursday   *Last Quarter*

7 Friday   HAYLEY AND ROY TUCKER MARRIED 2001
GREG TURNER DIED 2004

8 Saturday

9 Sunday   Mother's Day, USA, Canada, Australia and New Zealand

10	Monday	

11	Tuesday	MERIEL ARCHER BORN 2001

12	Wednesday	DEBBIE AND SIMON GERRARD MARRIED 2000 CLARRIE GRUNDY BORN 1954

13	Thursday	Ascension Day

14	Friday	*New Moon* **FIVE TRIAL EPISODES RECORDED 1950**

15	Saturday	

16	Sunday	

JACK WOOLLEY (ARNOLD PETERS)

17 Monday

18 Tuesday

19 Wednesday   Feast of Weeks (Shavuot)

20 Thursday   *First Quarter*

21 Friday

22 Saturday   NEIL CARTER BORN 1957

23 Sunday   Whit Sunday (Pentecost)

24 Monday   Holiday, Canada (Victoria Day)

---

25 Tuesday

---

26 Wednesday   JULIA AND LEWIS CARMICHAEL MARRIED 2005

---

27 Thursday   *Full Moon*

---

28 Friday

---

29 Saturday   LYNDA SNELL BORN 1947
JENNIFER AND BRIAN ALDRIDGE MARRIED 1976
***THE ARCHERS* FIRST BROADCAST IN MIDLAND REGION 1950**

---

30 Sunday   Trinity Sunday

31 Monday

1 Tuesday

2 Wednesday

Coronation Day

3 Thursday

Corpus Christi

4 Friday

Last Quarter

5 Saturday

6 Sunday

CHRISTOPHER CARTER (WILLIAM SANDERSON-THWAITE)

JUNE

7 Monday

Holiday, Republic of Ireland
Holiday, New Zealand (Queen's Birthday)

8 Tuesday

NIGEL PARGETTER BORN 1959
THE ARCHERS **FIRST BROADCAST IN STEREO 1992**

9 Wednesday

SID PERKS BORN 1944

10 Thursday

11 Friday

12 Saturday

New Moon
The Queen's Official Birthday (subject to confirmation)

13 Sunday

SIOBHAN HATHAWAY BORN 1965

JUNE

14 Monday   Holiday, Australia (Queen's Birthday)

15 Tuesday

16 Wednesday   RUTH ARCHER BORN 1968

17 Thursday   USHA GUPTA BORN 1962

18 Friday

19 Saturday   *First Quarter*
FALLON ROGERS BORN 1985

20 Sunday   Father's Day, UK, Canada and USA

JUNE

21 Monday

Summer Solstice (Summer begins)

---

22 Tuesday

ADAM MACY BORN 1967
CHRISTOPHER CARTER BORN 1988

---

23 Wednesday

---

24 Thursday

---

25 Friday

---

26 Saturday

Full Moon

---

27 Sunday

AMBRIDGE VIEW
The Carters

PRESENT DAYS

Upwardly mobile, outwardly much the same, Susan and Neil Carter were delighted to leave No 1, The Green and move into the house that Neil had built for them (with a little help from Mike Tucker). You can take the man from the pigs but never the pigs from the man and, despite all Susan's attempts, Neil managed to find himself a herd of pigs to tend and a disciple in Tom Archer to mentor.

Susan, however, is fast turning into a second Martha Woodford as she stands beady-eyed behind the counter in the Village Shop, dishing the dirt and ensuring the discomfort of most of her customers. Daughter Emma is divorced from William Grundy while son Christopher is now a qualified farrier and is fast developing into a babe magnet. Susan is especially delighted when he dates the likes of Alice Aldridge, although the reactions of Brian and Jennifer should there ever be a Carter in the family remains to be seen.

The Carter Family, left to right, Neil (Brian Hewlett), Christopher (William Sanderson-Thwaite), Emma (Felicity Jones), Susan (Charlotte Martin)

Is Neil a thwarted romantic or has Susan trained him? His surprise for their silver wedding anniversary surprised the audience as much as Susan. She would never imagine that Neil would think of a romantic night for two in London and he has set a hard example for the other men in Ambridge to follow. On the other hand Susan deserves a treat; she and Neil have shared a colourful past and endured much together.

Martha Woodford
(Mollie Harris)

PAST TIMES

- Ambridge View is the house of Susan's dreams but it came at a price. Neil designed it and Susan was given four bedrooms, an en-suite bathroom, downstairs loo, a utility room and patio doors. But they had to live in a caravan while the work was being done and it nearly ruined their relationship.

- Susan still has a way to go before she rivals Martha Woodford (Mollie Harris), who worked in the Village Shop, full and part-time, until 1996. Martha could prise information out of a stone, which certainly helped her talents as a fortune teller in the village fête.

- It's no surprise that a pig played its part in Neil and Susan's courtship. Susan won a pig at the Ambridge fete in 1983 and Neil offered to build a pen for it. The rest is history . . .

OFF AIR:
Mollie Harris, who played Martha Woodford, came from a poor family in the village of Ducklington in Oxfordshire. She wrote many books on country matters but the most famous is Cotswold Privies.

In 1993 Susan was sent to jail for six months. Her brother Clive had raided the Village Shop and he forced her to shelter him. The case made real life newspaper headlines as the sentence seemed so harsh, and a petition was set up to 'Save the Ambridge One'. It didn't work but it was a kind thought.

Brian Hewlett is an accomplished theatre and television actor and has a fabulous film credit: he played Lampredi in Roger Corman's highly acclaimed version of Edgar Allan Poe's The Masque of the Red Death, starring Vincent Price.

28 Monday

29 Tuesday

CAROLINE AND OLIVER STERLING MARRIED 2006

30 Wednesday

1 Thursday

Holiday, Canada (Canada Day)

2 Friday

3 Saturday

4 Sunday

Last Quarter
Independence Day, USA
JOLENE AND SID PERKS MARRIED 2002

---

5 Monday   Holiday, USA (Independence Day)

---

6 Tuesday

---

7 Wednesday

---

8 Thursday   LILIAN BELLAMY BORN 1947

---

9 Friday

---

10 Saturday

---

11 Sunday   *New Moon*
DORIS ARCHER BORN 1900

JULY

12 Monday

Holiday, Northern Ireland (Battle of the Boyne)

13 Tuesday

14 Wednesday

15 Thursday

St. Swithin's Day

16 Friday

17 Saturday

18 Sunday

First Quarter

JULY

WEEK 30
2010

19 Monday
JACK WOOLLEY BORN 1919

20 Tuesday
JAMIE PERKS BORN 1995

21 Wednesday

22 Thursday

23 Friday

24 Saturday

25 Sunday

26 Monday

Full Moon
SIPHO MADIKANE BORN 2007

27 Tuesday

28 Wednesday

29 Thursday

30 Friday

31 Saturday

1 Sunday

AUGUST

2 Monday

Summer Bank Holiday, Scotland
Holiday, Republic of Ireland

3 Tuesday

Last Quarter

4 Wednesday

5 Thursday

6 Friday

7 Saturday

EMMA GRUNDY BORN 1984
MATT CRAWFORD BORN 1947

8 Sunday

SHULA HEBDEN-LLOYD AND KENTON ARCHER BORN 1958

AUGUST

9 Monday

10 Tuesday   *New Moon*

11 Wednesday   First Day of Ramadân (subject to sighting of the moon)

12 Thursday   MARJORIE ANTROBUS DIED 2008

13 Friday

14 Saturday

15 Sunday

A LA CARTER
SUSAN CARTER

"I think the best way to start any sophisticated dinner party is with a good old fashioned favourite – prawn cocktail. Actually, I know that it's also one of Sabrina Thwaite's favourites, as she's often in the Village Shop *buying* a bottle of the Marie Rose Sauce. I'm so surprised at her; I always thought she had such excellent taste. *I* always make *my* sauce from scratch, as it tastes much better fresh . . ."

Serves 4

INGREDIENTS

500g (1lb 2oz) small cooked & peeled prawns (frozen will do)
Crisp lettuce leaves (e.g. Iceburg)
200ml (8 fl oz) mayonnaise
200ml (8 fl oz) salad cream
4 tbsp double cream
2 tbsp tomato ketchup
2 tsp lemon juice
A squeeze of tomato purée
A dash of Tabasco
A pinch of paprika

METHOD

- Mix together mayo, salad cream, double cream, tomato ketchup, lemon juice and Tabasco into a smooth pink paste.
- Thaw prawns carefully if frozen, drain and mix with sauce in a large bowl. Cover and put in fridge.
- To serve, shred lettuce and layer it in 4 glass bowls. Spoon on prawn mixture, sprinkle with paprika and add a wedge of lemon.

☆ SUSAN'S TOP TIP ☆

For special occasions garnish each glass with a large shelled prawn and serve with fine slices of buttered brown bread with the crusts removed. Bon appetit!

AUGUST

16 Monday	*First Quarter*

17 Tuesday	JULIA PARGETTER-CARMICHAEL BORN 1924

18 Wednesday

19 Thursday

20 Friday

21 Saturday

22 Sunday

AUGUST

---

23 Monday

---

24 Tuesday   *Full Moon*

---

25 Wednesday

---

26 Thursday

---

27 Friday   EMMA AND WILLIAM GRUNDY MARRIED 2004
                                                      USHA AND ALAN FRANKS MARRIED 2008

---

28 Saturday

---

29 Sunday

JENNIFER ALDRIDGE (ANGELA PIPER)

30 Monday   Summer Bank Holiday, UK (exc. Scotland)

31 Tuesday

1 Wednesday   *Last Quarter*

2 Thursday

3 Friday   LILIAN AND RALPH BELLAMY MARRIED 1971

4 Saturday

5 Sunday   Father's Day, Australia and New Zealand

6 Monday

Holiday, USA (Labor Day)
Holiday, Canada (Labour Day)

---

7 Tuesday

---

8 Wednesday

New Moon

---

9 Thursday

Jewish New Year (Rosh Hashanah)
Eid al-Fitr, Ramadân ends
(subject to sighting of the moon)

---

10 Friday

---

11 Saturday

CAROLINE AND GUY PEMBERTON MARRIED 1995

---

12 Sunday

SEPTEMBER

13 Monday   JOSH ARCHER BORN 1997

---

14 Tuesday

---

15 Wednesday   *First Quarter*

---

16 Thursday

---

17 Friday

---

18 Saturday   Day of Atonement (Yom Kippur)
JOE GRUNDY BORN 1921
DAVID ARCHER BORN 1959

---

19 Sunday

SEPTEMBER

20 Monday

---

21 Tuesday   SHULA AND MARK HEBDEN MARRIED 1985

---

22 Wednesday   *Full Moon*
Autumnal Equinox (Autumn begins)
First Day of Tabernacles (Succoth)
GRACE ARCHER DIED 1955

---

23 Thursday

---

24 Friday

---

25 Saturday

---

26 Sunday

WILLOW FARM
The Tuckers

PRESENT DAYS

Mike and Betty Tucker lived as tenants at Willow Farm, happily bringing up their two children until disaster struck when TB hit the herd. This awful shock was followed by a series of unfortunate events as the farm was sold, the Tuckers had to move and Mike's business began to fail. Eventually he was forced to declare himself bankrupt, and the family moved from pillar to post until, in 1988, Dr Matthew Thorogood leased Willow Farm back to them; home at last.

Several tumultuous years followed as the Tuckers struggled to make ends meet and, much to Mike's embarrassment, Betty had to take on cleaning and shop jobs to bring in the pennies. Luckily, things picked up for them in 1992 and, with the support of his friends and family, Mike got back on track, buying the farm the following year.

Mike bitterly missed Betty after her death in 2005 but has gradually got his life back together again and done his best for his family. When Roy and Hayley couldn't afford a home of their own he made the difficult decision to divide up Willow Farm to help out them out.

Mike Tucker (Terry Molloy)

Hayley (Lorraine Coady)

At first Brenda was horrified at the thought of diggers breaking up her home and carrying away precious memories of her mum, but Mike brought her round. Now Roy and Hayley live in Willow Farm with their children, while Mike and his new wife occupy the more modest building now known as Willow Cottage.

PAST TIMES

• Willow Farm was a fully working farm in the 1970s when it was owned by Haydn Evans who ran it with Tony Archer.

• Haydn offered Mike the rental of Willow Farm shortly after Betty discovered she was pregnant. Mike seized the opportunity with both hands, then used them to chop down the willow trees which inspired the farm's name.

• Neil Carter inherited a barn and eight acres of Willow Farm land from Bill Insley in 1986. He and Mike are good mates and he still uses the land to house some of his pigs and an organic free-range egg enterprise he runs with Hayley.

OFF AIR:
Few know that Ambridge's favourite one-eyed milkman has an interesting alter ego… Actor Terry Molloy performed the original Davros in the popular television series Doctor Who.

Actress Pamela Craig, who played Betty for many years, emigrated to New Zealand in 2005. Her departure created a sad storyline in The Archers *but we hear that Pam is very happy there.*

For a time actress Lorraine Coady was an English Lecturer at Bydgoszcz University, Poland. The system was quite different to what she was used to, though. When she moved all the desks out of the classroom for her first drama lesson, the students walked out, assuming she was having some sort of breakdown.

27 Monday

28 Tuesday

EDWARD GRUNDY BORN 1984

29 Wednesday

Michaelmas Day
ALICE ALDRIDGE BORN 1988
ELIZABETH AND NIGEL PARGETTER MARRIED 1994

30 Thursday

KATE MADIKANE BORN 1977

1 Friday

Last Quarter
OMNIBUS FIRST HEARD ON RADIO 4 1967

2 Saturday

GODFREY BASELY, CREATOR OF *THE ARCHERS*, BORN 1904
FIRST DAILY EPISODES ON RADIO 4 1967

3 Sunday

JILL ARCHER BORN 1930

OCTOBER

4 Monday   Holiday, Australia (Labour Day)

5 Tuesday

6 Wednesday

7 Thursday   *New Moon*

8 Friday

9 Saturday

10 Sunday   SUSAN CARTER BORN 1963

11 Monday

Holiday, Canada (Thanksgiving)
Holiday, USA (Columbus Day)

12 Tuesday

13 Wednesday

14 Thursday

First Quarter

15 Friday

16 Saturday

17 Sunday

OCTOBER

18 Monday	**ARCHERS ADDICTS FOUNDED 1990**

19 Tuesday	

20 Wednesday	

21 Thursday	

22 Friday	

23 Saturday	*Full Moon*

24 Sunday	United Nations Day GEORGE BARFORD BORN 1928 **FIRST EPISODE FROM THE MAILBOX BROADCAST 2004**

TOP TUCKER!
MIKE TUCKER

"Betty used to be the queen of the kitchen at Willow Farm, but I've learned a few tricks in the last few years. When I moved into Willow Cottage, I had to fend for myself a bit more. Now, when I can find the time, I do actually enjoy a bit of cooking. This toffee fudge banana recipe is dead easy, takes five minutes, and Phoebe loves it! If I can do it, anyone can, so why not have a go?"

Serves 4

INGREDIENTS

2 large, ripe bananas
50g (2oz) brazil nuts
375ml (¾ pint) double cream,
  whipped (fresh Guernsey
  of course)
150g (5oz) molasses sugar

METHOD

- Pre-heat the grill to its highest setting and brown brazil nuts for 3 minutes (take care not to burn them – it's easily done!)
- Peel and slice bananas. Place in large bowl and mix well with whipped cream then divide mixture into individual bowls or glasses.
- Sprinkle sugar over mixture then cover in clingfilm and put in fridge for a few hours.
- Chop up the nuts and sprinkle them on top to serve.

☆ MIKE'S TOP TIP ☆

I can't get enough of cream but, if you're watching your waistline like Hayley tells me I should, substitute cream with Greek yoghurt for a lower fat version.

OCTOBER

25 Monday

Holiday, Republic of Ireland
Holiday, New Zealand (Labour Day)
DORIS ARCHER DIED 1980

26 Tuesday

27 Wednesday

28 Thursday

29 Friday

30 Saturday

Last Quarter

31 Sunday

British Summer Time ends
Hallowe'en

NOVEMBER

1	Monday	All Saints' Day

2	Tuesday

3	Wednesday

4	Thursday

5	Friday	Guy Fawkes' Day

6	Saturday	*New Moon*

7	Sunday	JULIA PARGETTER-CARMICHAEL DIED 2005 **15,000TH EPISODE BROADCAST 2006**

NOVEMBER

8 Monday

9 Tuesday

10 Wednesday

11 Thursday

Holiday, USA (Veterans Day)
Holiday, Canada (Remembrance Day)

12 Friday

13 Saturday

First Quarter
PEGGY WOOLLEY BORN 1924

14 Sunday

Remembrance Sunday, UK
DANIEL HEBDEN-LLOYD BORN 1994
RUAIRI DONOVAN BORN 2002

MARJORIE ANTROBUS (MARGOT BOYD) WITH HER AFGHAN HOUNDS

NOVEMBER

15 Monday

16 Tuesday

JILL AND PHIL ARCHER MARRIED 1957

17 Wednesday

18 Thursday

19 Friday

THE ARCHERS FIRST BROADCAST ON THE INTERNET 1999

20 Saturday

BRIAN ALDRIDGE BORN 1943

21 Sunday

Full Moon
CLARRIE AND EDDIE GRUNDY MARRIED 1981

NOVEMBER

22 Monday

23 Tuesday

24 Wednesday

25 Thursday   Holiday, USA (Thanksgiving Day)

26 Friday

27 Saturday

28 Sunday   *Last Quarter*
First Sunday in Advent

29 Monday

30 Tuesday St. Andrew's Day

1 Wednesday MIKE TUCKER BORN 1949

2 Thursday Jewish Festival of Chanukah, First Day

3 Friday

4 Saturday

5 Sunday *New Moon*

6 Monday

7 Tuesday

8 Wednesday   Islamic New Year (subject to sighting of the moon)

9 Thursday

10 Friday

11 Saturday

12 Sunday

LUCY GEMMELL BORN 1971
PAT AND TONY ARCHER MARRIED 1974
LILY AND FREDDIE PARGETTER BORN 1999

DECEMBER

| 13 | Monday | *First Quarter* |

| 14 | Tuesday | ADAM MACY AND IAN CRAIG CIVIL PARTNERSHIP 2006 |

| 15 | Wednesday | RUTH AND DAVID ARCHER MARRIED 1988 |

| 16 | Thursday | BETTY TUCKER DIED 2005 |

| 17 | Friday | |

| 18 | Saturday | |

| 19 | Sunday | |

DECEMBER

20 Monday

21 Tuesday

Full Moon
Winter Solstice (Winter begins)
CHRISTINE BARFORD BORN 1931

22 Wednesday

23 Thursday

24 Friday

Christmas Eve
Holiday, USA
DEBBIE ALDRIDGE BORN 1970
SHULA AND ALISTAIR LLOYD MARRIED 1998

25 Saturday

Christmas Day

26 Sunday

Boxing Day (St. Stephen's Day)

THE GRUNDY FAMILY (LEFT TO RIGHT) ED (BARRY FARRIMOND), JOE (EDWARD KELSEY), EDDIE
(TREVOR HARRISON), CLARRIE (ROSALIND ADAMS), WILL (PHILIP MOLLOY)

27 Monday

Holiday, UK, Australia and New Zealand

28 Tuesday

Last Quarter
Holiday, UK and New Zealand
GODFREY BASELEY PRESENTED 'INTRODUCING *THE ARCHERS*' 1950

29 Wednesday

30 Thursday

31 Friday

New Year's Eve
Holiday, USA
JOHN ARCHER BORN 1975

1 Saturday

New Year's Day
JACK AND PEGGY WOOLLEY MARRIED 1991
***THE ARCHERS* FIRST BROADCAST NATIONWIDE 1951**

2 Sunday

NOTES

BORSETSHIRE BRAINTEASERS – SOLUTIONS

AMBRIDGE ANIMALS
CATTLE
GUERNSEY
FRIESIAN
HEREFORD

PIGS
BERKSHIRE
MIDDLEWHITE
GLOUCESTERSHIRE OLD SPOT

CREATURE COMFORTS WORDSEARCH
Joe's pony **Bartleby**
Eddie's ferret **Mrs. Archer**
Scarlett del Monte's boa constrictor **Bertie**
Christine's horse **Midnight**
Lynda's llama **Salieri**
The Bull peacock **Eccles**
Daniel's hamster **Harry**
Nigel's shire horse **Cranford Crystal**
One of Mrs. Antrobus' much loved afghans, **Bettina**
Alice's horse **Spearmint**
Laura Archers favourite duck, **Jemima**
Susan's prize pig, **Pinky**

YOU'RE AN ANIMAL!
NIGEL
LYNDA
TOM
HAYLEY
JAZZER
RUTH

```
E M F M A M E J B S O H E U C R P S
C I S R W I G J R E H C R A S R M A
S E V A L N P B S A T N Y T A F A R
P C O S I M I D N I G H T W L O N D
L C R E P A S M G I E O P R I Q B E
I L K A E B B I F R G S A C E E Q D
S E L R N M E T Y J P T K P R I O J
N S I J E F C S C E L N H T I F T S
B T A T S P O N A M K P I S E H A E
P K E L I R S R I A P E Y O S R C Y
O Y U B T D M N D E B W L A M T H B
R I A E M I S R B C A L R N J L R E
T P R T N V H L A L R T Y I E P O L
S H I T E I J M E A L Y C L M C V T
N T G I C C B L H O K J S D I B L R
A M C N L R S K Y N E T N T M P S A
Y R R A H T Y A I P X N E B A I R B
U E W R S R E P R A R S M O Y L T E
```

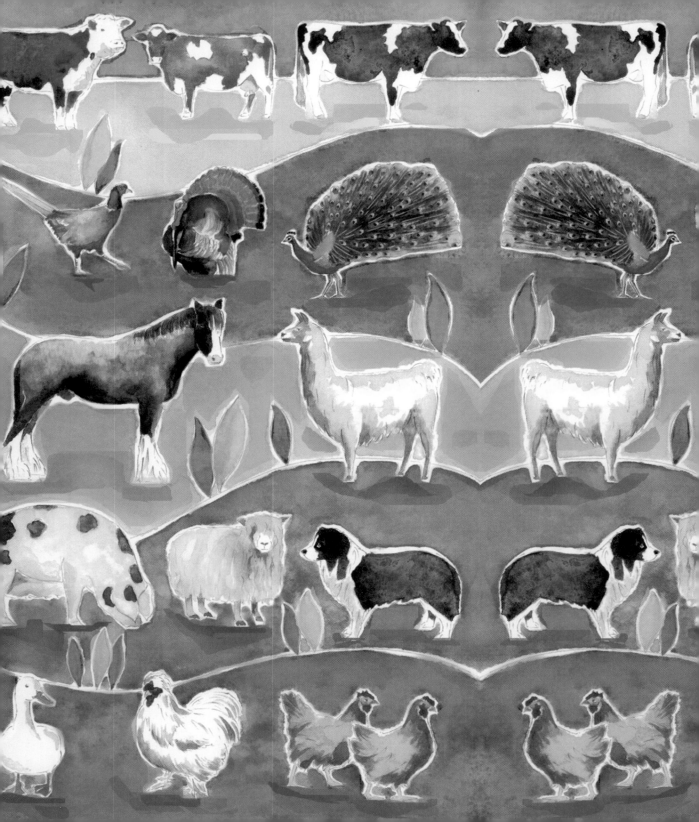